Christmas 1987
Ron Lezlie Emily

SWAMPED

SWAMPED

STANLEY BURKE*ROY PETERSON

Douglas & McIntyre
Vancouver/Toronto

Douglas & McIntyre Ltd.
1615 Venables Street
Vancouver, British Columbia
V5L 2H1

Canadian Cataloguing in Publication Data

Burke, Stanley, 1923–
Swamped

ISBN 0-88894-565-5

1. Canada – Commerce - United States - Anecdotes, facetiae, satire, etc. 2. United States - Commerce - Canada - Anecdotes, facetiae, satire, etc. 3. Free trade and protection - Anecdotes, facetiae, satire, etc. I. Peterson, Roy, 1936-. II. Title.
FC173.B87 1987 382.'0971'073'0207 C87-091271-2
F1026.4.B87 1987

Cover art by Roy Peterson
Typeset by Vancouver Typesetting Co. Ltd.
Printed and bound in Canada by D. W. Friesen & Sons Ltd.

The Swamp was going to be different — prouder, richer, more united and businesslike.

And it all seemed so easy. Do it like the Eagles, the richest of animals. Don't do it like the Gliberals.

Now, children, for 50 years, the Gliberals had run the Swamp, and they had run it into the ground — drained it and given it away to their friends. But at last the Ordinary Animals realized what was happening and gave power back to the commonsense Preservatives led by rich, handsome Brian Bullrooney.

Now Brian Bullrooney had been head of the great Iron Orb Corporation, which was owned by the Eagles, so he knew their secrets. He knew how to get rich.

"Brian Bullrooney knows how to make money," said the Ordinary Animals. "He'll know how to make money for us too."

"And he'll make even more for us!" shouted the Yuppies.*

* Young Upstart Pups.

TRADE
SWAMP
神
風
神

The animals had become fed up with their previous leader, Peter Waterhole. He had been born with the family silver in his mouth and spent the animals' clams travelling around the world with his sons Just-On, Right-On and Bang-On. In the end they dumped him, and he sank leaving only a rose floating like a memory.

With Brian Bullrooney, the animals were sure it would be different, and his soft, sincere voice reassured them that at last they had made the right choice.

Brian Bullrooney agreed with them.

"This is going to be a piece of *gateau* — *une pièce de* cake," he said, effortlessly speaking the Swamp's two languages. Brian Bullrooney, you see, was the perfect Swampian politician because he was a Beaver who came from the Land of the Frogs and knew how to make money.

"I can't fail!" he said.

He had, however, one gnawing doubt caused by creatures in the far-off land of Nip-On — which got its name because its animals had a yen for nipping on other people's markets. Even the mighty Eagles were afraid.

But wealthy though they were, the Nip-On-Easies were small, polite animals who bowed and smiled, and Brian Bullrooney couldn't take them entirely seriously.

TODAY'S RESULTS

Anyway, there was work to be done and he couldn't wait to get at it. Starting as a poor young animal, he had worked his way to the top of Iron Orb. Now he would run the Swamp with the same dedication, and all the animals would be rich.

The Ordinary Animals believed him and it showed on the Poles. Nothing in the Swamp was more important than the Poles because they showed how the Ordinary Animals were thinking. Each had a wise Pole-Star sitting on top, and these Pole-Stars would ask the Ordinary Animals questions. They would write down the answers and stick them on their Poles, and each day the Elected Animals would read them. In this way they, too, knew as much as the Ordinary Animals, and this was why they were called Poleticians.

Brian Bullrooney had his own Star Pole-Star who poled all the other Pole-Stars. This meant that the Chief Minister knew more than anyone.

To make things even better, he appointed his best friends to the Chief Minister's Office, and every day they pondered what the Pole-Stars said and gave the Chief Minister friendly advice.

"*Fantastique!*" said Brian Bullrooney. "I can't go wrong."

His Grande Plan was simple.

First, he would make friends with Ronald Raygun, the President of the Eagles, and persuade him to sign a Spree Trade Agreement.

"Spree Trade made the Eagles rich and it will make us rich too," said Brian Bullrooney. "It's the only way to fly."

Then he would fire all the Gliberals who infested the Swamp. Next he would fire as many civil serpents and bureaucrabs as possible and bring in entrepreneurs* who would make money for the Swamp.

Finally, he would inspire the Ordinary Animals to work as hard as the animals did in the Land of the Eagles and in Nip-On.

"In five years the Swamp will be rich, the animals will be grateful, and I'll be re-elected forever!" he exclaimed.

Getting to know the President would be easy because Ronald Raygun's forefathers, like Brian Bullrooney's, came from a feisty, boggy place called Ire-Land. So Brian Bullrooney invited the Chief Eagle to a wonderful party at the Chateau Front 'n' Back on St. Bogrick's Day.

The most talented animals in the Swamp sang and danced, and the All-Swamp Broadcasting Corporation was paid to carry it so the animals could see how well their new leader was doing.

The best part was when Brian Bullrooney and Ronald Raygun sang "When Ire-ish Eyes Are Smiling," which they did very well. Ronald Raygun, you see, had been an actor in a sacred place called Holy Wood, and he harmonized beautifully with Brian Bullrooney's deep, melodious voice, especially on the sentimental last line, "Sure it steeeeealls your heart away."

* From the Frog, meaning "between-the-takers" — because the entrepreneur stands in the middle and takes from both sides.

WE LOVE
EAGLES!
YO!
EAGLES!
COME
AND
GIT IT!
EAGLES
COME
BACK
R.I.P.
Fear-us

Mind you, it was necessary to steal away a couple of million clams to pay for everything but, if it bought the friendship of the Chief Eagle, it was worth it.

"They couldn't do better than this in Holy Wood," thought Brian Bullrooney as he jutted his jaw jauntily.

"Do it like the Eagles," he said once again.

Next he called Allan Got-Lip, the Swampian ambassador in Washingtub, and told him to make a splash.

Then he got rid of Fear-Us, a terrifying organization created by Peter Waterhole to frighten away the Eagles and their money. The Eagles, you see, owned so much of the Swamp that it worried the animals, especially the Yackademics, the Intellect-You-Alls and the Socialbusts, who all belonged to the Trendy Party — the Trendy P.

Peter Waterhole himself had been a Socialbust, so he had called together a number of animals who disliked the Eagles and put them in charge of keeping out Eagle money.

Unfortunately the scheme worked, and soon Ordinary Animals were losing their jobs.

"Don't worry," said Brian Bullrooney, smiling smoothly. "I'll fix everything."

So, after burying Fear-Us, he went along the southern edge of the Swamp nailing up signs saying "Eagles Come Back!" and "We Love Eagles!"

Before he was able to finish, however, a few little problems developed, and the irresponsible News Hounds started howling. First, someone left a package of dead fish on his doorstep, and some of the animals complained about the smell.

WIN-A-PIG
AIR
WIN-A-PIG
AIR
1

Well, that was cleaned up, but then his Defence Minister was found with a Lady Animal of the Evening in a Nightie Club and had to resign.

Then there was that ridiculous outcry about a small jail to be built at Bay Promo, the Chief Minister's home town.

"It may cost a little more," the Chief Minister told the animals credibly. "But think of the advantages. I'll be able to visit the prisoners and see they're well looked after."

"It will be handy to visit your friends," muttered a *sage derrière** at the back of the room.

Worse still was the business about the Swamp-18 flying machine contract which went, quite properly, to a Frog company called Swampair. The Gophers thought it should have gone to a Win-A-Pig company on the flimsy grounds that they could do it cheaper and better.

"Can't you see this is in the higher interest of the Swamp?" he asked the outraged Gophers. "The Swamp needs the Preservatives and the Preservatives need the Frogs. Be reasonable. Be patriotic. *Vive le Swamp!*"

But of course the Swamp Creatures weren't reasonable. And a few thought that Brian Bullrooney's jaw was looking funny.

* A Frog phrase literally meaning "wise behind," or "wise words from the rear." See also *demi-derrière*.

"It seems to be growing larger!" they said.

Meanwhile the News Hounds were chasing in a great pack from one end of the Swamp to the other, sniffing for imaginary evil.

Even more irresponsible were the members of the Loyal Proposition, the non-Preservative members of the House of Come-Ons who were loyally dedicated to the proposition that the government is always wrong. Like the News Hounds, the Loyal Proposition overlooked everything that was right and exaggerated everything that was wrong. The Ordinary Animals believed what they were told.

Brian Bullrooney was furious — and several animals said his jaw was growing.

What annoyed him most was that all this nonsense took up his time and he wasn't able to get on with cutting the deficit. This was desperately necessary because the Gliberals had spent all the clams in the Swamp and Brian Bullrooney had promised to find some new ones.

"Maybe we could take a few from the Old Age Animals," he suggested. "They'll never notice."

"Never notice??!!" screamed the Old Age Animals, and they hobbled off to Nottalot, the capital, as fast as their canes and crutches would take them. As the Gliberals and Trendy P's cheered and the News Hounds rushed around waving wooden microphones, they stormed the House of Come-Ons and, when it was over, they agreed they hadn't had so much fun since the Boar War.

The best part of all was when Brian Bullrooney came out and assured them there had been a terrible mistake.

"I didn't say we'll *take* it from the Old Age Animals," he said sincerely. "My goodness, I said we'll *make* it for all you wonderful animals who made the Swamp what it is!"

"*Je vous aime!*" he added in the other language to be quite sure no one was offended.

And everyone could see that his jaw really was growing.

Then Brian Bullrooney realized with horror that he was slipping on the Poles.

The News Hounds, of course, howled gleefully, and the slip became a slide.

Brian Bullrooney's advisors panicked and shouted so much conflicting advice that he fired them and hired professionals. The News Hounds howled even more, and the slide became a dive.

Brian Bullrooney was outraged. After all he had done for the Swamp, how could the animals treat him this way?

How could the Swamp be united?

Uniting the Swamp was supposed to be the job of the All-Swamp Broadcasting Corporation, but it was having its own problems because it had always supported the Gliberals and the Trendy P.

"After all," said the administrators of the Corporation, "how can you support the Preservatives? All they care about is results."

But now the Preservatives were in power and were asking why they should shell out a billion clams to see Gnowlton Gnash chomp on the news every night.

"Suppose the Preservatives sell *us?*" whimpered the All-Swamp administrators. "What would we do then?"

In this crisis, Pierre D'You Know, the head of the nitwork, acted decisively. The program "Labouring for You" was replaced by "Clam Dig"; "Freedom Now" was suppressed in favour of "Hymn Sing"; and reporters were told to wear five-piece suits. Most important of all, a giant wooden computer was installed to look after the accounts.

"We will be more Preservative than the Preservatives," said Pierre D'You Know. For a lifelong Gliberal, this would be difficult but, as an experienced civil serpent, he could handle it.

ON
OFF
ALL-SWAMP
COMPUTER

Unfortunately the computer blew out its wooden brains and, appearing before the House of Come-Ons, Pierre D'You Know had to admit he didn't know where the clams went.

"They're not lost," he said. "It's just that we can't find them."

He would have been fired, but the Preservatives were too busy worrying about other things.

Like Doom Petroleum.

The Gliberals had put one billion clams into Doom under the impression that swamp oil would go to a hundred clams a barrel — maybe even a thousand.

"We'll all be rich," said the starry-eyed Meander-Ins, the most exalted of civil serpents, so named because of the effortless way they meandered in and out of the chambers of power trailing clouds of bureaucratic glory. They were the Gods of Nottalot.

"Today Doom, tomorrow the World!" they cried in deliriums of joy during lunch at the Realdough Club.

Soon, of course, the bottom fell out of swamp oil prices and the Meander-Ins moved to new dreams. Like holding their jobs.

SPREE TRADE
GOTCHA

Meanwhile, Brian Bullrooney was lonely and frightened as he listened to the terrifying sound of the Media Pack baying in the night on the National News. Half his ministers had been fired, his friends were gone from the CMO, and the Ordinary Animals were laughing at him. What could he do? Even another pair of Gotcha shoes didn't help.

"Get me my new Pole-Star!" he screamed.

"The only friends you have left are the Capitalusts," the Star Pole-Star told him, "and Spree Trade is what they want."

Now the Capitalusts were more important than anybody because they created the jobs that paid the Ordinary Animals and, even more, dug up the clams that elected the Preservatives.

"Look after the Capitalusts and the Capitalusts will look after the Swamp," Brian Bullrooney had always said.

So he called all the Preservative members to a Revival Meeting at Screech Lake and told them to go out and sell Spree Trade.

"William Lyin' MacKenzie Sting said it long ago — Buy Them with Their Own Money," he reminded the Gories. "We'll do better. We'll buy them with the Eagles' money!"

By now, Allan Got-Lip was making waves in Washingtub, and Mrs. Got-Lip had a particularly striking reputation. This was the time to go for it, so Brian Bullrooney appointed Simon Greaseman and told him to start oiling the works.

The Eagles were fierce but Greaseman was tough, and Brian Bullrooney was sure he would put them on the skids.

Some animals were outraged, however. They said Spree Trade would destroy their dream of a Paradise behind the Dam. The great Dam had been started by the Beaver pioneers long ago, just after their conquest of the Frogs, and generations of descendants had laboured to build it ever higher and stronger. Now, secure behind its towering wall, they were sure they could keep their own special place.

"Keep out the Eagles! Keep out the world! Rally round the Dam!" these patriots cried.

Across the Swamp, the Yackademics, the Intellect-You-Alls and the Pondits had taken up the cry. But others disagreed.

"What good does the Dam do us?" asked the Capitalusts, which was rather odd because the Dam was originally built to protect them.

"It doesn't help us sell the seeds we work so hard to gather," said the Gophers in the Western Meadow.

"It doesn't help us sell swamp oil," echoed the Marmots in the Great Western Hills.

"It doesn't help us sell fish!" cried the Lobsters and Codfish at the Eastern end.

"Or trees!" came the plaintive voice of the forgotten Otters rising up from the far side of the Western Hills.

JOHN
ED
ME
GOTCHA

The Codfish were particularly annoyed because the civil serpents in Nottalot had just given a lot of their fish away to two little islands called Sea Air and Sneak-Along that belonged, for some strange reason, to the Motherland of the Frogs. The civil serpents had given the fish away, furthermore, without consulting the Codfish who were, as the saying goes, "fished off."

Brian Bullrooney was sure Spree Trade was the answer that would unite the Swamp, make it rich and vault him back to the top of the Poles.

He put in a call to Simon Greaseman in Washingtub.

"Simon," he said, trying to sound relaxed and confident, "how's it going on Spree Trade? We've got to get results."

"Sorry, Chief Minister," said Greaseman. "Nothing doing on Spree Trade. The Eagles are in a flap about Nip-On. They're selling too much here."

"*Merde!*" said Brian Bullrooney, using a deeply religious Frog expression meaning "*mère de Dieu*."

To make things worse, that night when he was doing his homework at 24 Nossex Drive, his Dam office rang to tell him he was lying flat at the bottom of the Poles while Ed Badly-Bent cavorted at the top.

SWAMPTOWN
REALTY

"At least I can't go down from here," he consoled himself.

But he did.

First, André Bison-Nyet, his Minister of Moving Things, was caught moving land for the Early Con Corporation, so he had to go.

Then there was the discovery that the Swamp was being bought up by the Pandas as well as the Nip-On-Easies.

Most of the Pandas in the Swamp came from an island called King Koin, to which they fled when their homeland, the Land of the Great Dragon, was taken over by the Come-You-Nits. There was nothing much to do on the island, so making money became their way of life, and they worked even harder than the Nip-On-Easies. Life was good, but they feared the dread Come-You-Nits might also take over King Koin, so many moved to the Swamp. The Swamp Creatures had never seen such wealth and were astounded to find King Koin entrepreneurs so rich they had Swampian entrepreneurs as houseboys.

"Who's going to end up owning the Swamp?" Brian Bullrooney wondered. "King Koin, Nip-On, the Eagles or the Swamp Creatures?"

The Swampians, clearly, were running fourth — but Brian Bullrooney had no time to worry about that.

"You've got to get a Success, any Success," the Star Pole-Star told him. "You went down the last Pole as though it was greased."

Constitution
X
SIGN HERE
GOTCHA

"What can I do?" wailed the Chief Minister, slapping his tail in despair. "Spree Trade isn't working. I can't fix the economy, and I can't buy the animals because I haven't any clams."

"Hmmmm," thought the Star Pole-Star, wondering if his own bill would be paid. "I've got to think of something. What about getting the Frogs to sign the Constitution? That wouldn't cost much."

"Brilliant!" said Brian Bullrooney, and he went to work feverishly. Using all the skills he had learned as a negotiator at Iron Orb, he persuaded the Frogs to hop on board. He almost gave away the Swamp to do it but, as he said, "Anything for a deal."

At this point Peter Waterhole, mischievous as ever, resurfaced to put a thorn in poor Brian Bullrooney's side. Fortunately, few paid attention, and Brian Bullrooney was able to announce triumphantly that the leaders from all ten corners of the Swamp had agreed — with him.

The Swamp was united, and Brian Bullrooney had a Success.

The Poleticians all congratulated themselves on being able to agree on something, and the All-Swamp Broadcasting Corporation ran endless commentaries. The Pondits and the Intellect-You-Alls took it very seriously and said wise things, but unfortunately the Ordinary Animals weren't much interested, and Brian Bullrooney remained at the bottom of the Poles.

Real disaster hit when the lobbyists in Washingtub went on the warpath!

Now, lobbyists are animals who lob things at Poleticians, and in Washingtub they are very good at it. The lobbyists were angry because Nip-On was selling too much to the Land of the Eagles and even angrier because Nip-On refused to buy anything in return on the ridiculous grounds that things the Eagles made cost too much and didn't work well.

Then the Eagles discovered that the Swamp Creatures were better at cutting down trees and they, too, were getting more and more business.

"Put up a barricade!" screeched the Eagles.

Soon the Eagles were building barricades everywhere and, to their horror, the Swamp Creatures realized what was happening.

The Eagles were building their *own* Dam!

"But what about Free Competition?" cried the Swamp Creatures.

"Of course we're for Free Competition," replied the Eagles sharply. "We only object when it costs money."

"But . . . but . . . you can't build a *Dam!*" cried the Swamp Creatures. "That's what *we* do. Eagles sit around in trees looking fierce."

The Eagles paid no attention and went on fiercely building their Dam. Poor Brian Bullrooney gnashed his teeth in fury when he heard the news.

"Dam nation!" he shouted. "They're mad at Nip-On so they attack us! Get me the President!"

Unfortunately President Raygun was not available.

"He's thinking about the Bears today," said Allan Got-Lip. "That's all he can handle."

The Bears, you see, were the Eagles' enemies who lived far to the north. The Bears were Come-You-Nits, which meant they believed all animals were equal and should live in the same-sized dens and eat the same food — except Party Members, of course.

The Eagles said this was Evil and that everyone should struggle against the Bears. All animals should have the same chance, they said, to be big and strong and get to the top of the tree. Those on top would have the most room and the most food and those below would get the leftovers. The Eagles called this Equality of Opportunity.

To defend this dream, President Raygun worked out a wonderful plan called Tar Wars. Under this plan, the Eagles would lob barrels of tar at the Bears, which would cause so much mess the Bears would never dare start anything.

"What a blow for peace!" exclaimed the President.

Next, Ronald Raygun punished a nasty dictator called Colonel Go-Daffy of Lip-Ya, and the Eagles loved it! Now he would declare peace on Nick-Your-Agua and guarantee his place in history.

All this would be done so the Ordinary Eagles, who had suffered many humiliations, would again be able to preen themselves and stand tall.

"I'll get an Oscar for this," he told himself. "It's my greatest role."

Then, just as he was coming to his triumphant final scene, disaster struck.

First, the Bears got an unscrupulous leader called Mikhail Grab 'n' Shove who grabbed control and started shoving peace proposals down the throats of the Eagles. This outraged the President.

"How can you stand tall if the enemy won't stand tall against you?" he demanded. "Untrustworthy! Just like all Come-You-Nits."

DESIGNATED LOOSE CANNON

As if that weren't bad enough, word leaked about a wonderful plan he had devised with a band of Patriots to free hostages in I-Ran and send money to the Freedom Fighters in Nick-Your-Agua.

It was run by a fine young officer named Ollie Oddball who made a deal with Madman Kash-Only, the famous arms dealer, to send guns to the I-ugh-Told-You How-Many in I-Ran. In return, the I-ugh-Told-You sent money to Switch-Your- Land, where it was washed and pressed by Gnomes and sent, squeaky-clean, to the Freedom Fighters.

The plan had to be kept secret because, well, the Ordinary Eagles wouldn't understand. Actually, Members of the Congers wouldn't understand either — nor, for that matter, would the Media Eagles. It required Patriots but, alas, there were few Patriots left.

When the story broke, the President had to say he didn't know anything about it and, my goodness, he really didn't. After all, the President knows about things in a general sort of way, but he didn't really *know* — if you know what I mean.

But that's not the way it sounded at the Grand Inquisition chaired by Senator Annoy-Ya.

The President bravely withstood the attack but finally fell from his birdhouse and lost his face.

He never flew again.

The greatest of Eagle Presidents was thus destroyed like his predecessor, Richard Millstone Nix 'Em. Brian Bullrooney's plan was in ruins, and his desperation made his previous desperation seem lighthearted.

"Get me another Pole-Star," he croaked.

The newest Pole-Star, he was assured, was the Absolute All-Star Pole-Star.

"Tell me, what can I do?" anguished the Chief Minister as the new seer materialized.

"Well," said the wizard, casually tossing his pointed hat into the corner, "with 101 per cent accuracy 21 times out of 20, our Poles show no one can run the Swamp. The Gliberals blew it. Now you're blowing it. Next, the animals will try the Trendy P and they'll blow it completely. The only chance you've got is to give the Swamp away."

"Give it away?" said Brian Bullrooney. "That's against Preservative policy. We don't give anything away!"

"You want to get re-elected?" asked the All-Star Pole-Star, firing up the little wooden computer built into his briefcase. "Then you've got to give the Swamp to the Ordinary Animals. More clams for Baby Animal Care Centres. More clams for the Old Age Animals."

ON
STRIKE
風
AIR NIPON

"But we haven't got any clams!" agonized Brian Bullrooney.

"Dig some up," said the Pole-Star as statistics started pouring out of his briefcase. "Think of it this way. You're giving the Swamp back to its owners. In return, they give you back your government. Everybody's happy. Everybody wins. That's the Preservative way."

"I hadn't thought of it like that," said Brian Bullrooney.

That made Brian Bullrooney feel better, and he stopped worrying.

He stopped worrying about the drowning Lobsters, about the Gophers who were in the hole, and about the Marmots who no longer whistled because the price of swamp oil was lower than a grasshopper's belly.

He was deeply moved, though, by the plight of the poor Otters who once had been rich and fun-loving but now were destitute. Their beautiful city of Vansnoozer was owned by the Pandas and filled with rich tourists from Nip-On who came to take pictures of the quaint natives.

The Nip-On-Easies, you see, rewarded their hardest-working workers by sending them on holidays to the Swamp where they were fascinated to find workers who didn't work.

They were told these animals were members of the Bunions, so called because of the pain they caused. The Bunions had long struggled for eradication of the scourge of work and, in preparation for that glorious day, went on regular holidays called Strikes. Now that the Swamp was sinking, however, it was evident that achievement of this noble goal would be somewhat delayed, so the Bunions instead struck to maintain wages. These Strikes were successful and made many of their members the most highly paid unemployed in the world.

BOTTOM LINE $
BOTTOM LINE $
BOTTOM LINE $
BOTTOM LINE $
BOTTOM LINE $

All this was difficult for the workers from Nip-On to understand but, when the meaning got through, they were delighted.

"This means no competition for us," they said. "Bang-Zai, Swamp!"

And they climbed back into their tour busses and headed for the next picturesque place.

They were happy, but back home in Nip-On their leaders worried, especially about the Pandas. The Pandas were the most numerous of animals and, for centuries, had been rich and powerful but now had fallen on hard times.

The final blow had come from their recent leader, Chairman Wow, with his Little Red Book containing wise sayings like "Go Right by Going Left!" and "Stand Firm While Marching Resolutely Forward!" The Pandas resolutely tried to follow these instructions, but ended up on their ying-yangs and were only saved by a new leader, Chairman Ping Pong, with a new slogan: "The Only Thing That Matters Is the Bottom Line Under the Wise Guidance of the Party."

This worried the leaders of Nip-On because they thought it just might work. Furthermore, they worried that the Pandas in the Land of the Great Dragon might get together with those on King Koin. Even worse, they both might be joined by wealthy Pandas on another island called Tie-One-On.

"If all those Pandas ever gang up, it will be a bear market for us," exclaimed the Nip-On-Easies.

"What to do?" said their leader, Premier Pack-A-Sony.

SWAMP SECTION #103A
SWAMP SECTION #102A
SWAMP SECTION #101 A
SWAMP SECTION #100A

A small committee of 500 studied the question and made a recommendation. "We must get the Swamp before the Pandas do," they said.

Nip-On, you see, was digging up vast pieces of the Swamp and shipping it home where they used it to make things. If the Pandas owned the Swamp, these supplies would be cut off.

Furthermore, Nip-On needed the Swamp as a holiday retreat.

"But most of all," said the committee, "we need the Swamp's Dam, the best Dam in the world. This will protect us against the Eagle's Dam."

"Ah so!" exclaimed Premier Pack-A-Sony. "But how do we get the Swamp?"

"Tow it to Nip-On," said the committee.

And so it was done. The Swamp went west to the Far East.

Nottalot, however, was left behind because it didn't seem to do anything, and so it remains a lonely island in an empty ocean.

The animals there didn't even notice.

To this very day, children, if you go to that strange, forgotten place, you will still hear the division bells sounding across the water, Members shouting at one another, and the sound of the Speaker crying "Order! Order!"

High above the towers and turrets and ramparts, you will see, shimmering in the mist, a giant jaw with a great ghostly smile.

And a voice, resonant as a foghorn, echoes endlessly across the water:

"Everything's going fine. Believe me!"